Let's Talk Maths

for ages 5–7

Andrew Brodie ✔

Contents

Introduction   3

Year 1 Activity 1: Read numbers to 20, relating these to a number track and identifying 1 more and 1 less   6

Year 1 Activity 2: Read numbers beyond 20, relating these to a number line and identifying 1 more and 1 less, and 10 more or 10 less for multiples of 10   8

Year 1 Activity 3: Use a number track to relate addition to counting on   10

Year 1 Activity 4: Use a hundred square for understanding subtraction as finding a difference by counting up   12

Year 1 Activity 5: Visualise and name common 2-D shapes   14

Year 1 Activity 6: Sort shapes into groups according to a given criterion; suggest a different criterion for grouping the same objects   16

Year 1 Activity 7: Derive and recall addition facts for totals to at least 5   18

Year 1 Activity 8: Derive and recall subtraction facts for 3, 4 and 5   20

Year 1 Activity 9: Derive all pairs of numbers with a total of 10   22

Year 1 Activity 10: Work out subtractions from 10   24

Year 1 Activity 11: Solve problems involving counting, adding, subtracting, doubling or halving in the context of numbers or money   26

Year 1 Activity 12: Solve problems involving counting, adding, subtracting, doubling or halving in the context of numbers or money   28

Year 1 Activity 13: Present outcomes using pictograms   30

Year 1 Activity 14: Present outcomes using block graphs   32

Year 1 Activity 15: Use vocabulary related to time; order days of the week   34

Year 1 Activity 16: Use vocabulary related to time; order months of the year   36

Year 1 Activity 17: Use the vocabulary of halves and quarters in context   38

Year 1 Activity 18: Read the time to the hour and half-hour   40

Year 2 Activity 1: Read and compare two-digit numbers   42

Year 2 Activity 2: Describe and extend number sequences and recognising odd and even numbers   44

Year 2 Activity 3: Count up to 100 objects by grouping them and counting in tens, fives or twos   46

Year 2 Activity 4: Use a hundred square for adding or subtracting mentally a one-digit number or a multiple of 10 from any two-digit number   48

Year 2 Activity 5: Read and compare three-digit numbers   50

Year 2 Activity 6: Solve problems involving adding, subtracting or multiplying in the context of numbers or money   52

Year 2 Activity 7: Derive and recall all addition and subtraction facts for each number to at least 10   54

Year 2 Activity 8: Derive and recall all addition and subtraction facts for pairs of numbers with a total of 20   56

Year 2 Activity 9: Derive and recall all addition and subtraction facts for pairs of multiples of 10 up to 100   58

Year 2 Activity 10: Derive and recall multiplication facts for the 2 times table and related division facts   60

Year 2 Activity 11: Derive and recall multiplication facts for the 5 times table and related division facts   62

Year 2 Activity 12: Derive and recall multiplication facts for the 10 times table and related division facts   64

Year 2 Activity 13: Identify reflective symmetry in patterns and 2-D shapes   66

Year 2 Activity 14: Visualise common 2-D shapes; sort, make and describe shapes   68

Year 2 Activity 15: Present and interpret outcomes using block graphs   70

Year 2 Activity 16: Recognise and use whole, half and quarter turns, both clockwise and anticlockwise   72

Year 2 Activity 17: Read the time to the hour, half-hour and quarter hour   74

Year 2 Activity 18: Derive and recall doubles of all numbers to 20   76

Year 2 Activity 19: Understand that halving is the inverse of doubling   78

This series of three books will help every school in the delivery of 'a renewed focus on oral and mental mathematics' as recommended in the Rose Review and the Williams Review of Mathematics Teaching.

The Rose Review of the primary curriculum (April 2009) recommends:

> *Primary schools should make sure that children's spoken communication is developed intensively within all subjects and for learning across the curriculum.*

The Review of Mathematics Teaching states that the existing curriculum for mathematics is well balanced and should continue in its current form but it adds:

> *Two issues only are singled out: the need for an increased focus on the 'use and application' of mathematics and on the vitally important question of the classroom discussion of mathematics. It is often suggested that 'mathematics itself is a language' but it must not be overlooked that only by constructive dialogue in the medium of the English language in the classroom can logic and reasoning be fully developed – the factors at the very heart of embedded learning in mathematics.*

In considering pedagogy the Review notes:

> *It must be truly interactive, giving children time, for example, to think, to question as well as answer, to discuss and to try out their own ideas and strategies.*

> *The critical importance of engaging children in discussing mathematics is widely recognised. This, of course, includes learning and using mathematical language. Talking mathematics should not be seen simply as a rehearsal in class of the vocabulary of mathematics, novel and important though that may be for the young learner. It should extend to high quality discussion that develops children's logic, reasoning and deduction skills, and underpins all mathematical learning activity. The ultimate goal is to develop mathematical understanding – comprehension of mathematical ideas and applications.*

How to use this book

Let's Talk Maths provides opportunities for teachers to use, and reuse, stimulating whiteboard displays that encourage pupils to discuss mathematics using appropriate mathematical vocabulary.

Each double-page spread in the teachers' notes features detailed instructions, including questions to prompt discussion, on how to use the CD content and a screenshot of the typical view that the children will see on the interactive whiteboard. The teachers' notes specify the prior learning that the children need, together with learning objectives and success criteria. The notes also give an indication for which Blocks the activity is suitable.

How to use the CD

Choose an activity from the main menu:

Activity navigation:

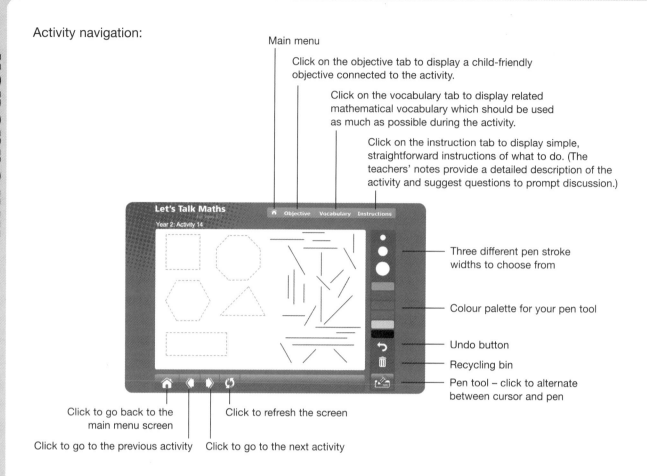

Main menu

Click on the objective tab to display a child-friendly objective connected to the activity.

Click on the vocabulary tab to display related mathematical vocabulary which should be used as much as possible during the activity.

Click on the instruction tab to display simple, straightforward instructions of what to do. (The teachers' notes provide a detailed description of the activity and suggest questions to prompt discussion.)

Let's Talk Maths
Year 2: Activity 14

Objective   Vocabulary   Instructions

Three different pen stroke widths to choose from

Colour palette for your pen tool

Undo button

Recycling bin

Pen tool – click to alternate between cursor and pen

Click to go back to the main menu screen

Click to refresh the screen

Click to go to the previous activity

Click to go to the next activity

Speaking and Listening in Key Stage 1

This is the first book in the series and is designed to be used with children in Years 1 and 2. As you will have read on page 3, the importance of encouraging children to listen carefully and to speak appropriately in all aspects of the curriculum is reflected in national guidance for the teaching of mathematics. Opportunities are found for engaging pupils in speaking and listening activities in each unit of the teaching blocks specified in the Guidance for Planning for Year 1 and Year 2. Suggestions for incorporating most of the learning objectives for 'Speaking', 'Listening and responding' and 'Group discussion and interaction' specified in the Primary Framework for Literacy are linked to specific units for mathematics:

Year 1 Speaking

■ Tell stories and describe incidents from their own experience in an audible voice
   Block C Unit 1

■ Retell stories, ordering events using story language
   Block D Units 1 and 3, Block E Unit 1

■ Experiment with and build new stores of words to communicate in different contexts
   Block D Unit 2

Year 1 Listening and responding

■ Listen with sustained concentration
   Block B Unit 1

■ Listen to and follow instructions accurately, asking for help if necessary
   Block A Unit 2

- Listen to tapes or videos and express views about how a story or information has been presented
  Block E Unit 2

Year 1 Group discussion and interaction

- Take turns to speak, listen to others' suggestions and talk about what they are going to do
  Block B Unit 2

- Ask and answer questions, make relevant contributions, offer suggestions
  Block A Unit 1

- Explain their views to others in a small group, and decide how to report the group's views to the class
  Block C Unit 3, Block E Unit 3

Year 2 Speaking

- Speak with clarity and intonation when reading and reciting texts
  Block A Units 1 and 2

- Tell real or imagined stories (using conventions of familiar story language)
  Block B Unit 3

- Use language and gesture to support the use of models, diagrams or displays when explaining
  Block B Unit 2 (Note that this objective is worded differently to the corresponding objective in the Framework for English.)

Year 2 Listening and responding

- Listen to others in class, ask relevant questions and follow instructions
  Block B Unit 1, Block C Unit 1 and Block D Units 1, 2 and 3

- Listen to a talk by an adult, remember some specific points and identify what they have learned
  Block E Units 1 and 2

- Respond to presentations by describing characters, repeating some highlights and commenting constructively
  Block A Unit 3

Year 2 Group discussion and interaction

- Ensure everyone contributes, allocate tasks, consider alternatives and reach agreement
  Block C Unit 2

- Explain their views to others in a small group; decide how to report the group's views to the class
  Block C Unit 3 (Note that this objective is worded differently to the corresponding objective in the Framework for English.)

- Adopt appropriate roles in small or large groups and consider alternative courses of action
  Block E Unit 3 (Note that this objective is worded differently to the corresponding objective in the Framework for English.)

Read numbers to 20, relating these to a number track and identifying 1 more and 1 less

Building on previous learning

Before starting this unit check that the children can already:

☐ match sets of objects to numerals that represent the number of objects

☐ say and use number names in order in familiar contexts

☐ know that numbers identify how many objects are in a set

☐ count reliably up to 10 everyday objects

☐ estimate how many objects they can see and check by counting

☐ count aloud in ones

☐ recognise numerals 1 to 9

Learning objectives

■ Read numerals from 0 to 20

■ Use knowledge of place value to position these numbers on a number track

■ Say the number that is 1 more or 1 less than any given number

Learning outcomes

The children will be able to:

■ read all numerals from 0 to 20

■ relate all these to the number track

■ state the number that is 1 more or 1 less than a specified number

■ use appropriate vocabulary

■ talk confidently about the numbers

Success criteria

Can the children…

☐ read confidently the numbers pointed out to them?

☐ identify the number that is 1 more or 1 less than any of the numbers shown?

☐ count out loud from 0 to 20?

☐ listen and talk confidently using some of the vocabulary listed and some of the question types shown?

How to use the material for discussion

The adult should start with asking questions to provide a structure but should try to withdraw from the discussion and allow the children to take over so that they are asking questions of each other. They will, at times, need to be reminded of the appropriate vocabulary and you may wish to encourage them to use the vocabulary listed.

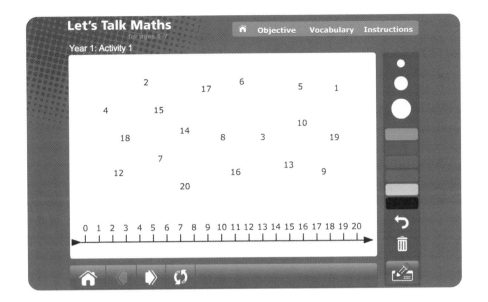

Click on each number to highlight it for discussion.

The activity could open with questions of the following type:

- What is this number? Can you read this number?
- Which of the numbers have one digit?
- Which of the numbers have two digits?
- How many digits does this number have?

If you feel that the children are confident, different questions can be used:

- How do these numbers (pointing to the one-digit numbers) look different to these numbers (two-digit numbers)?
- What number is one more than this number?
- What number is one less than this number?
- Can you count up from this number?
- Can you count on to 20 from this number?

Appropriate vocabulary

show me	read	count
count to	count on	count on to
count on from	count up to	count up from
compare	order	more
less	biggest	smallest
before	after	zero, one, two, three, etc.
'teens' number	explain	digit

Read numbers beyond 20, relating these to a number line and identifying 1 more and 1 less, and 10 more or 10 less for multiples of 10

Building on previous learning

Before starting this unit check that the children can already:

- [ ] match sets of objects to numerals that represent the number of objects
- [ ] say and use number names in order in familiar contexts
- [ ] know that numbers identify how many objects are in a set
- [ ] count reliably up to 10 everyday objects
- [ ] estimate how many objects they can see and check by counting
- [ ] count aloud in ones
- [ ] recognise numerals 1 to 20

Learning objectives

- Read numerals from 0 to 40
- Use knowledge of place value to position these numbers on a number line
- Say the number that is 1 more or 1 less than any given number, and 10 more or 10 less for multiples of 10
- Compare and order numbers using the related vocabulary

Learning outcomes

The children will be able to:

- read all numerals from 0 to 40
- relate all these to the number line
- state the number that is 1 more or 1 less than a specified number
- state the number that is 10 more or 10 less than a multiple of 10
- use appropriate vocabulary
- talk confidently about the numbers

Success criteria

Can the children…

- [ ] read confidently the numbers pointed out to them?
- [ ] identify the number that is 1 more or 1 less than any of the numbers shown?
- [ ] identify the number that is 10 more or 10 less than any of the multiples of 10?
- [ ] listen and talk confidently using some of the vocabulary listed and some of the question types shown?

How to use the material for discussion

The adult should start with asking questions to provide a structure but should try to withdraw from the discussion and allow the children to take over so that they are asking questions of each other. They will, at times, need to be reminded of the appropriate vocabulary and you may wish to encourage them to use the vocabulary listed.

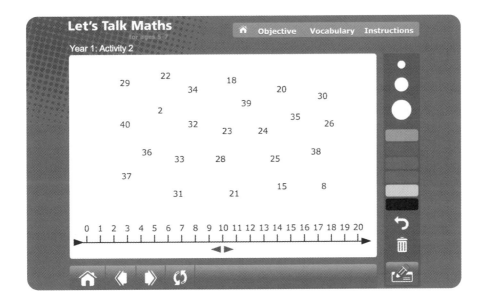

Click on each number to highlight it for discussion.

The activity could open with questions of the following type:
- What is this number? Can you read this number?
- Which of the numbers has one digit?
- How many digits does this number have?
- Which is the smallest number?
- Which is the biggest number?
- Which of the numbers have two tens?
- Which of the numbers have zero ones?

If you feel that the children are confident, different questions can be used:
- How do these numbers (pointing to numbers with 2 tens) look different to these numbers (numbers with 3 tens)?
- What number is one more than this number?
- What number is one less than this number?
- What number is ten more than this number? (Pointing to a multiple of 10)
- What number is ten less than this number? (Pointing to a multiple of 10)
- Can you count up from this number?
- Can you count on to 40 from this number?
- Look at these two numbers. Which one is bigger? Which one is smaller?

Appropriate vocabulary

show me	read	count
count to	count on	count on to
count on from	count up to	count up from
compare	order	more
less	biggest	smallest
before	after	zero, one, two, three, etc.
'teens' number	explain	digit

Use a number track to relate addition to counting on

Building on previous learning

Before starting this unit check that the children can already:

☐ count reliably at least 20 objects, recognising that when rearranged the number of objects stays the same

☐ compare and order numbers, using the related vocabulary

☐ read and write numerals from 0 to 20 then beyond; use knowledge of place value to position these numbers on a number track and number line

☐ use the vocabulary related to addition and symbols to describe and record addition number sentences

Learning objectives

- Relate addition to counting on
- Recognise that addition can be done in any order
- Use the vocabulary related to addition to describe addition number sentences
- Use the appropriate symbols to record addition number sentences

Learning outcomes

The children will be able to:

- count on to solve an addition question
- rearrange the numbers in a question to make the counting on operation easier
- use appropriate vocabulary to describe addition number sentences
- use symbols to record addition number sentences

Success criteria

Can the children...

☐ count on to find answers to questions such as 26 + 5, 37 + 4, 5 + 7, 16 + 8?

☐ make decisions regarding which number to start from when answering questions such as 8 + 35, 19 + 8, 9 + 38, 27 + 5?

☐ talk about the addition process for the above questions, using the appropriate vocabulary?

☐ write appropriate addition sentences to record the additions?

How to use the material for discussion

This activity is ideal for the whole class but could readily be used with a smaller group, reinforcing the pupils' counting skills and providing practice in using the 'counting on' method for addition. It promotes lots of opportunities for pupils to speak and listen, using the appropriate vocabulary.

Note that the number track shown on the presentation is designed to be used before the children are introduced to the hundred square. Some children find the hundred square confusing as the 'higher' numbers are positioned 'lower' on the square – eg the number 53 is physically below the 43. The number track used here provides an excellent introduction to the layout of the hundred square, which appears on the next presentation.

Note that you could also use this number track for the objective of understanding subtraction as 'take away' and finding a difference.

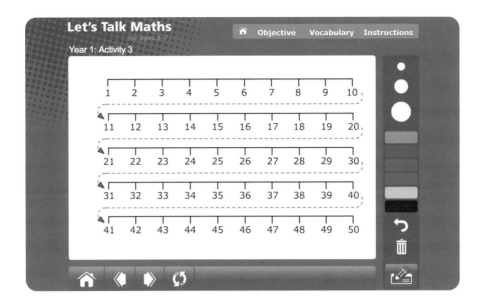

Start with some introductory activities:

- 'Let's start at 1 and count all the way to 20.' Point at the numbers as the children say them together.
- 'Now let's start at 20 and count to 30.'
- 'What is this number?' (pointing at any random number, eg 36)
- 'What number is 1 more than 36?'
- 'What number is 1 less than 36?'

Now move on to the main objectives of the activity – counting on for addition, deciding the number to start from and, of course, using appropriate mathematical language. Discuss the process, using the range of vocabulary interchangeably, as this example shows:

- 'What is this number?' (pointing at any random number, eg 29)
- 'I would like to add 4 to 29. What's 29 plus 4? Let's find out on the number track.'

At this point you could invite a pupil to come out and point to 29. Ask her to add 4 by counting on. Ensure that she starts with her finger on 29, then says 'one' as she points to 30, 'two' as she points to 31, etc. When she reaches 33, discuss the answer: 'Well done. 29 add 4 is 33. 29 plus 4 is 33. 33 is 4 more than 29.' Write down the question for pupils to see: 29 + 4 = 33. Talk about this written representation.

Now encourage the pupils to make up some questions to ask the group about the number track, modelled on the one that you have discussed with them. Some children will suggest questions such as: 7 + 29 = Show the children how it is easier to start at the 29 and count on 7, than to start at 7 and count on 29. Encourage the children to make their own decisions regarding which number to start at, using questions such as:

- 8 + 35, 19 + 8, 9 + 38, 27 + 5

Appropriate vocabulary

zero, one, two, …, fifty	count on	count up to
more	less	larger
bigger	greater	fewer
smaller	add	more
plus	make	sum
total	altogether	equals
sign	tens	'teens' number

Use a hundred square for understanding subtraction as finding a difference by counting up

Building on previous learning

Before starting this unit check that the children can already:

☐ count reliably at least 20 objects, recognising that when rearranged the number of objects stays the same

☐ compare and order numbers, using the related vocabulary

☐ read and write numerals from 0 to 20 then beyond; use knowledge of place value to position these numbers on a number track and number line

☐ use the vocabulary related to subtraction and symbols to describe and record subtraction number sentences

Learning objectives

■ Understand subtraction as 'take away' and finding a difference by counting up

Learning outcomes

The children will be able to:

■ use practical equipment for the process of taking away

■ count up on the hundred square to find a difference

■ use appropriate vocabulary to describe subtraction number sentences

■ use symbols to record subtraction number sentences

Success criteria

Can the children…

☐ use practical equipment to complete the process of subtraction by taking away?

☐ use appropriate vocabulary for the take away process?

☐ use the hundred square to find differences by counting up?

☐ use appropriate vocabulary for the process of finding a difference?

How to use the material for discussion

You may wish to work with the children on the process of 'taking away' using practical equipment, ensuring that the appropriate vocabulary is used.

A hundred square is displayed on the whiteboard. You could remind the pupils of the number track that they have seen in Activity 3 as this provides an excellent introduction to the layout of a hundred square.

After starting the discussion by questioning the pupils yourself, encourage individual pupils to ask questions of the group. Ensure that all pupils use appropriate vocabulary.

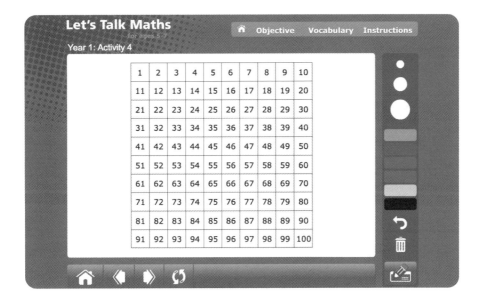

Start with some introductory activities:

- 'Let's start at 20 and count up to 50.' Point at the numbers as the children say them together.
- 'Now let's start at 80 and count back to 60.'
- 'What is this number?' (pointing at any random number, eg 97)
- 'What number is 1 more than 48?'
- 'What number is 1 less than 89?'
- 'What number is 10 more than 50?'
- 'What number is 10 less than 70?'

Now discuss the process of finding the difference between two numbers, using the range of vocabulary interchangeably, as this example shows:

- 'What is the difference between 32 and 26?'
- 'What is 32 subtract 26?'
- 'How much more is 32 than 26?'
- 'How much less than 32 is 26?'
- '32 minus 26.'

Now encourage the pupils to make up some questions to ask the group about the hundred square, modelled on the one that you have discussed with them.

Appropriate vocabulary

zero, one, two, ..., hundred	count up to ... from ...	difference
more	less	larger
bigger	greater	fewer
smaller	subtract	minus
take away	leaves	difference
equals	how much more is	how much less is
sign	tens	'teens' number

Visualise and name common 2-D shapes

Building on previous learning

Before starting this unit check that the children can already:

☐ use familiar objects and common shapes to create and recreate patterns and build models

☐ use language such as 'circle' or 'bigger' to describe the shape and size of solids and flat shapes

☐ use everyday words to describe position

Learning objectives

■ Visualise and name common 2-D shapes and describe their features

Learning outcomes

The children will be able to:

■ name the following shapes: circle, triangle, square, rectangle

■ describe the features of each of the shapes

Success criteria

Can the children…

☐ identify each of the shapes shown on the presentation?

☐ describe the number of sides of the triangle, square, rectangle?

☐ describe the number of corners of the triangle, square, rectangle?

☐ explain that the circle has only one side and no corners?

☐ explain that the circle has a curved side and the other shapes have straight sides?

How to use the material for discussion

Discuss one of the shapes, referring to the number of sides, the number of corners, whether the sides are straight or curved, etc.

You could extend the activity by providing the pupils with some 3-D solids and encouraging them to ask similar questions, this time referring to faces, edges and points.

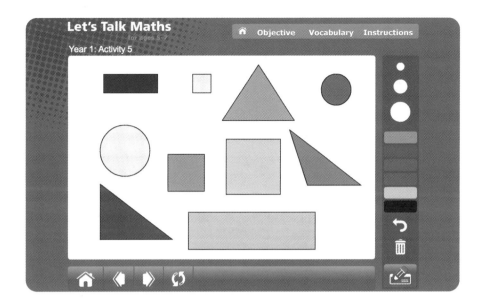

Pick one of the shapes at random and ask the pupils questions such as:

- How many sides has this shape got?
- How many corners has this shape got?
- Are the sides straight or curved?

Ensure that all pupils use appropriate vocabulary when they answer the questions.

Now ask one of the children to discuss the same aspects of another shape – encourage the child to ask questions of the others.

Appropriate vocabulary

explain	count	compare
property	shape	make
curved	straight	side
corner	square	triangle
circle	rectangle	draw
build	flat	point
face	edge	cube
cuboid	pyramid	cone
cylinder	sphere	

Sort shapes into groups according to a given criterion; suggest a different criterion for grouping the same objects

Building on previous learning

Before starting this unit check that the children can already:

☐ use familiar objects and common shapes to create and recreate patterns and build models

☐ use language such as 'circle' or 'bigger' to describe the shape and size of solids and flat shapes

☐ use everyday words to describe position

☐ sort familiar objects to identify their similarities and differences

☐ count how many objects share a particular property, presenting results using pictures, drawings or numerals

Learning objectives

■ Visualise and name common 2-D shapes and describe their features

■ Sort shapes into groups according to a given criterion

■ Suggest a different criterion for grouping the same shapes

Learning outcomes

The children will be able to:

■ name the following shapes: circle, triangle, square, rectangle

■ describe the features of each of the shapes

■ sort them into groups based on a particular property

■ choose another property as a basis for sorting

Success criteria

Can the children...

☐ identify each of the shapes shown on the presentation?

☐ describe the number of sides of the triangle, square, rectangle?

☐ describe the number of corners of the triangle, square, rectangle?

☐ explain that the circle has only one side and no corners?

☐ explain that the circle has a curved side and the other shapes have straight sides?

☐ use different criteria for sorting the shapes?

How to use the material for discussion

Discuss one of the shapes, referring to the number of sides, the number of corners, whether the sides are straight or curved, etc. Ask the pupils to identify the name of the shape then ask them to drag all of those shapes into the sorting area. Encourage them to say clearly what shapes are in the sorting area and what shapes are outside it.

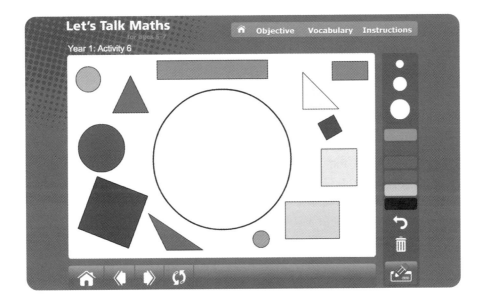

Pick one of the rectangles and ask the pupils questions such as:

- How many sides has this shape got?
- How many corners has this shape got?
- Are the sides straight or curved?

Ensure that all pupils use appropriate vocabulary when they answer the questions.

Now ask them to find all the other rectangles and to drag them into the sorting area. Encourage them to identify the properties of the rectangles and to identify the names of the shapes that are outside of the sorting area.

Ask one of the children to pick a different shape and to ask the other pupils about it. Can they sort all of these shapes into the sorting area?

Appropriate vocabulary

explain	count	compare
property	shape	make
curved	straight	side
corner	square	triangle
circle	rectangle	draw
build	flat	point
face	edge	cube
cuboid	pyramid	cone
cylinder	sphere	sort

Derive and recall addition facts for totals to at least 5

Building on previous learning

Before starting this unit check that the children can already:

☐ count reliably at least 20 objects, recognising that when rearranged the number of objects stays the same

☐ compare and order numbers, using the related vocabulary

☐ read and write numerals from 0 to 10

☐ select two groups of objects to make a given total of objects

Learning objectives

■ Derive and recall all pairs of numbers with a total of 3, 4 or 5

■ Use the vocabulary related to addition and symbols to describe and record addition number sentences

■ Use the equals sign

Learning outcomes

The children will be able to:

■ recall all pairs of numbers with a total of 3, 4 or 5

■ write addition number sentences using the add sign (+) and equals sign (=)

Success criteria

Can the children…

☐ create number sentences on screen using the numerals and symbols?

☐ find all of the combinations of pairs of numbers that have a total of 3, 4 or 5?

How to use the material for discussion

This activity concerns discussion of number sentences based on the children's prior knowledge that each numeral represents a specific number of objects. Some children will need further practice in combining sets of objects for counting.

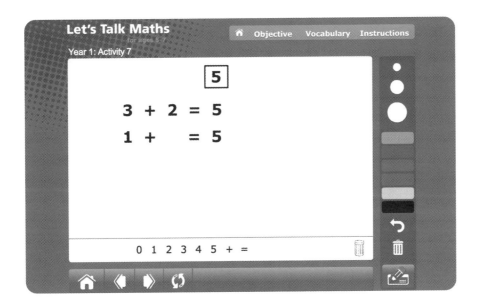

Discuss the number 5 with the children. Explain that they will be finding pairs of numbers that make 5 altogether. You could use a range of vocabulary to describe this, eg: finding two numbers that add together to equal 5, finding two numbers that have a total of 5, finding two numbers that have a sum of 5.

Ask the children to take turns to come to the whiteboard to drag a number to start a number sentence. Ask the first child to ask another one what to put next, ie the + sign, then to ask another child what number should be put next, etc. As with all of these activities, encourage each child to ask the questions clearly using the appropriate vocabulary.

Once all the children have found all the addition facts for 5, ask them to find the addition facts for 3, then for 4.

Appropriate vocabulary

zero, one, two, …, five	count	pair
more	less	larger
bigger	greater	fewer
smaller	add	more
plus	make	sum
total	altogether	equals
sign	explain	number sentence
write	record	the same number as

Derive and recall subtraction facts for 3, 4 and 5

Building on previous learning

Before starting this unit check that the children can already:

- [ ] count reliably at least 20 objects, recognising that when rearranged the number of objects stays the same
- [ ] compare and order numbers, using the related vocabulary
- [ ] read and write numerals from 0 to 10
- [ ] select two groups of objects to make a given total of objects
- [ ] understand subtraction as take away and as find a difference

Learning objectives

- Work out subtractions from 3, 4 or 5
- Use the vocabulary related to subtraction and symbols to describe and record subtraction number sentences
- Use the equals sign

Learning outcomes

The children will be able to:

- work out all subtractions from 3, 4 and 5
- record subtractions using subtraction number sentences containing the minus sign (-) and equals sign (=)

Success criteria

Can the children...

- [ ] create number sentences on screen using the numerals and symbols?
- [ ] find all subtractions from 3, 4 or 5?

How to use the material for discussion

This activity concerns discussion of number sentences based on the children's prior knowledge that each numeral represents a specific number of objects. Some children will need further practice in 'taking away' objects from a set of objects.

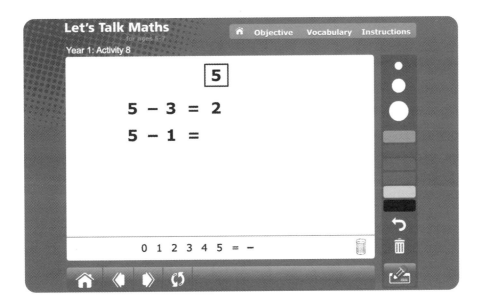

Discuss the number 5 with the children. Explain that they will be subtracting numbers from 5 and give an example, such as 5 - 3 = 2. You could use a range of vocabulary to describe this example, eg: 5 subtract 3 is 2; 5 take away 3 leaves 2; 5 minus 3 is 2; the difference between 5 and 3 is 2.

Ask the children to take turns to come to the whiteboard to drag a number to start a number sentence. Ask the first child to ask another one what to put next, ie the - sign, then to ask another child what number should be put next, etc. As with all of these activities, encourage each child to ask the questions clearly using the appropriate vocabulary.

Once all the children have found all the addition facts for 5, ask them to find the addition facts for 3, then for 4.

Appropriate vocabulary

zero, one, two, ..., five	count	pair
more	less	larger
bigger	greater	fewer
smaller	subtract	minus
take away	make	leaves
equals	sign	explain
number sentence	write	record

Derive all pairs of numbers with a total of 10

Building on previous learning

Before starting this unit check that the children can already:

☐ count reliably at least 20 objects, recognising that when rearranged the number of objects stays the same

☐ compare and order numbers, using the related vocabulary

☐ read and write numerals from 0 to 10

☐ select two groups of objects to make a given total of objects

Learning objectives

- Derive all pairs of numbers with a total of 10
- Use the vocabulary related to addition and symbols to describe and record addition number sentences
- Use the equals sign

Learning outcomes

The children will be able to:

- derive all pairs of numbers with a total of 10
- write addition number sentences using the add sign (+) and equals sign (=)

Success criteria

Can the children…

☐ create number sentences on screen using the numerals and symbols?

☐ find all of the combinations of pairs of numbers that have a total of 10?

How to use the material for discussion

This activity concerns discussions of number sentences based on the children's prior knowledge that each numeral represents a specific number of objects. Some children will need further practice in combining sets of objects for counting.

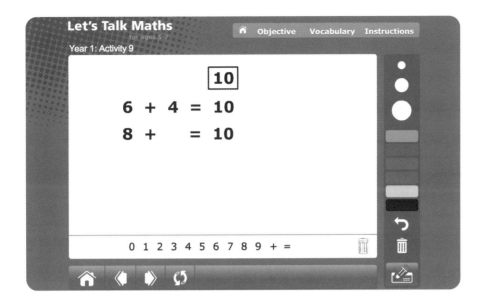

Discuss the number 10 with the children. Explain that they will be finding pairs of numbers that make 10 altogether. You could use a range of vocabulary to describe this, eg: finding two numbers that add together to equal 10, finding two numbers that have a total of 10, finding two numbers that have a sum of 10.

Ask the children to take turns to come to the whiteboard to drag a number to start a number sentence. Ask the first child to ask another one what to put next, ie the + sign, then to ask another child what number should be put next, etc. As with all of these activities, encourage each child to ask the questions clearly using the appropriate vocabulary.

As an extension activity, you could ask the children to create similar number sentences for 9, 8, 7 etc.

Appropriate vocabulary

zero, one, two, ..., ten	count	pair
more	less	larger
bigger	greater	fewer
smaller	add	makes
plus	make	sum
total	altogether	equals
sign	explain	number sentence
write	record	the same number as

Work out subtractions from 10

Building on previous learning

Before starting this unit check that the children can already:

☐ count reliably at least 20 objects, recognising that when rearranged the number of objects stays the same

☐ compare and order numbers, using the related vocabulary

☐ read and write numerals from 0 to 10

☐ derive and recall all pairs of numbers with a total of 10

☐ select two groups of objects to make a given total of objects

☐ understand subtraction as take away and as find a difference

Learning objectives

■ Work out the subtractions from 10

■ Use the vocabulary related to subtraction and symbols to describe and record subtraction number sentences

■ Use the equals sign

Learning outcomes

The children will be able to:

■ work out all subtractions from 10

■ record subtractions using subtraction number sentences containing the minus sign (-) and equals sign (=)

Success criteria

Can the children…

☐ create number sentences on screen using the numerals and symbols?

☐ find all the subtractions from 10?

How to use the material for discussion

This activity concerns discussion of number sentences based on the children's prior knowledge that each numeral represents a specific number of objects. Some children will need further practice in 'taking away' objects from a set of objects.

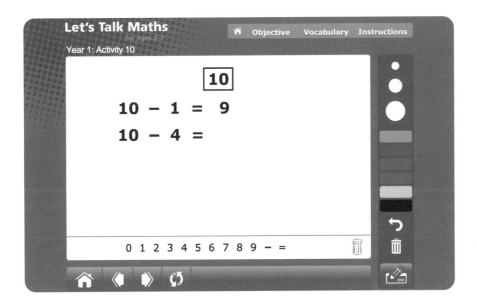

Discuss the number 10 with the children. Explain that they will be subtracting numbers from 10 and give an example, such as 10 - 3 = 7. You could use a range of vocabulary to describe this example, eg: 10 subtract 3 is 7; 10 take away 3 leaves 7; 10 minus 3 is 7; the difference between 10 and 3 is 7.

Ask the children to take turns to come to the whiteboard to drag a number to start a number sentence. Ask the first child to ask another one what to put next, ie the - sign, then to ask another child what number should be put next, etc. As with all of these activities, encourage each child to ask the questions clearly using the appropriate vocabulary.

As an extension activity, you could ask the children to create similar number sentences for 9, 8, 7 etc.

Appropriate vocabulary

zero, one, two, ..., ten	count	pair
more	less	larger
bigger	greater	fewer
smaller	subtract	minus
take away	make	leaves
equals	sign	explain
number sentence	write	record

Blocks A, B, D, E and revision

Solve problems involving counting, adding, subtracting, doubling or halving in the context of numbers or money

Building on previous learning

Before starting this unit check that the children can already:

- [ ] derive and recall all pairs of numbers with a total of 10
- [ ] derive and recall addition facts for totals to at least 5
- [ ] work out the corresponding subtraction facts
- [ ] count on or back in ones, twos, fives and tens
- [ ] relate addition to counting on
- [ ] understand subtraction as take away and find a difference by counting up
- [ ] use the vocabulary related to addition and subtraction and symbols to describe and record addition and subtraction number sentences
- [ ] use the equals sign

Learning objectives

- Solving problems involving adding in the context of money
- Solving problems involving subtracting in the context of money

Learning outcomes

The children will be able to:

- find total amounts to pay for two items
- find change when buying an item

Success criteria

Can the children…

- [ ] add together two sums of money in pence to find the total cost of two priced items?
- [ ] find the change from 10 pence or 20 pence when buying some priced items?
- [ ] use appropriate vocabulary in relation to spending money and finding change?

How to use the material for discussion

The priced fruits can be used for a variety of problem-solving questions: for comparing prices, for finding the total cost of two or more items, for finding change from 10p or 20p.

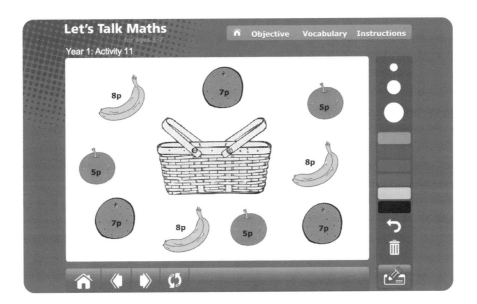

Discuss the items of fruit, asking questions and dragging the appropriate fruits into the shopping basket:

- Which costs more, a banana or an apple?
- How much more does an orange cost than an apple?
- What is the difference in price between an apple and an orange?
- What is the price of two bananas?
- What is the total cost of a banana and an apple?
- If I buy an orange, how much change would I have from 10p?

Now encourage one of the pupils to ask some questions about buying the fruit.

Appropriate vocabulary

more	less	total
cost	altogether	difference
price	change	double
answer	explain	operation

Solve problems involving counting, adding, subtracting, doubling or halving in the context of numbers or money

Building on previous learning

Before starting this unit check that the children can already:

- [ ] derive and recall all pairs of numbers with a total of 10
- [ ] derive and recall addition facts for totals to at least 5
- [ ] work out the corresponding subtraction facts
- [ ] count on or back in ones, twos, fives and tens
- [ ] relate addition to counting on
- [ ] understand subtraction as take away and find a difference by counting up

Learning objectives

- Solving problems involving adding in the context of money
- Solving problems involving subtracting in the context of money

Learning outcomes

The children will be able to:

- find totals in the context of coins
- make comparisons between different amounts of money

Success criteria

Can the children…

- [ ] find the total amounts represented by two or by three coins?
- [ ] compare different amounts of money?

How to use the material for discussion

Talk about each child shown on the presentation and the amount of money in his/her purse. If possible use some real coins to show the amounts, ensuring that the pupils can correctly identify each coin and can add together the numbers represented by the coins.

Discuss each child and how much is in his/her purse:

- What coins does Tom have?
- How much does Tom have altogether?
- How much more would Tom need to make 20p?
- How much would Tom have if he spent 10p?

Once the pupils are confident in stating the amount in each purse, they can make comparisons about the amounts each child has:

- Who has the most money?
- Who has the least money?
- How much would Beth need to give to Tom so that they both have the same amount?

Now encourage one of the pupils to ask some questions about the children and their coins.

Appropriate vocabulary

more	less	total
coins	altogether	difference
money	how much more?	how much less?
answer	explain	amount
most	least	equal amount

Present outcomes using pictograms

Building on previous learning

Before starting this unit check that the children can already:

- [ ] sort familiar objects to identify their similarities and differences
- [ ] count how many objects share a particular property, presenting results using pictures, drawings or numerals
- [ ] understand subtraction as find the difference

Learning objectives

- Solving problems involving adding in the context of numbers
- Solving problems involving subtracting in the context of numbers
- Presenting outcomes using pictograms
- Answering a question by recording information in lists and tables

Learning outcomes

The children will be able to:

- find totals in the context of numbers of pets
- make comparisons between different numbers of pets
- contribute to the creation of a pictogram
- interpret the information on a pictogram

Success criteria

Can the children...

- [ ] contribute to the creation of a pictogram?
- [ ] interpret the information on the pictogram?
- [ ] use appropriate vocabulary when interpreting data?

How to use the material for discussion

Before doing the activity, discuss collecting information about pets. Ask the children to state whether they have a pet but explain that information is being collected about cats, dogs, hamsters, rabbits and fish. Ask how many people have a cat and invite a child who is not a cat owner to count the number of cat owners, etc. Gather the information on a table or chart for the children to refer to when you discuss the creation of the pictogram.

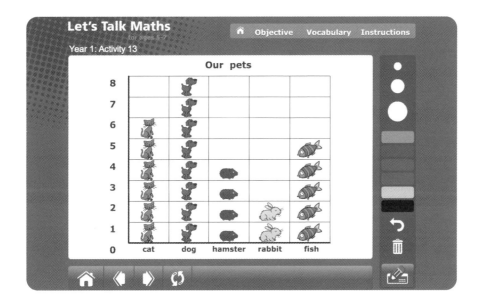

Invite pupils to come to the whiteboard and enter the data that you have collected so that the pictogram is completed. Ask questions about the pictogram, eg:

- How many cats are there?
- What is the most common pet?
- What is the least popular pet?
- How many more dogs are there than fish?
- How many fewer hamsters are there than cats?
- How many cats and dogs are there altogether?

Appropriate vocabulary

problem	question	collect
organise	compare	order
sort	group	different
represent	interpret	count
tally	information	graph
pictogram	list	table
label	title	more
less	most common	least common
most popular	least popular	how many more?
how many fewer?		

Year 1 Activity 14

Present outcomes using block graphs

Building on previous learning

Before starting this unit check that the children can already:

- [ ] sort familiar objects to identify their similarities and differences
- [ ] count how many objects share a particular property, presenting results using pictures, drawings or numerals
- [ ] understand subtraction as find the difference

Learning objectives

- Solving problems involving adding in the context of numbers
- Solving problems involving subtracting in the context of numbers
- Presenting outcomes using block graphs
- Answering a question by recording information in lists and tables

Learning outcomes

The children will be able to:

- find totals in the context of favourite drinks
- make comparisons between different favourites
- contribute to the creation of a block graph
- interpret the information on a block graph

Success criteria

Can the children...

- [ ] contribute to the creation of a block graph?
- [ ] interpret the information on the block graph?
- [ ] use appropriate vocabulary when interpreting data?

How to use the material for discussion

Before doing the activity, discuss collecting information about favourite drinks.
Ask the children to make a choice between coke, lemonade, orange juice or milk.
Gather the information on a table or chart for the children to refer to when you
discuss the creation of the block graph.

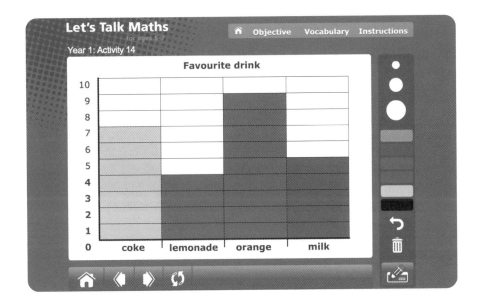

Invite pupils to come to the screen and enter the data that you have collected so that the block graph is completed. Ask questions about the graph, eg:

- How many people prefer coke?
- What is the most popular drink?
- What is the least popular drink?
- How many more people like orange than like milk?
- How many fewer people like lemonade than like coke?

Appropriate vocabulary

problem	question	collect
organise	compare	order
sort	group	different
represent	interpret	count
tally	information	graph
block graph	list	table
label	title	more
less	most common	least common
most popular	least popular	how many more?
how many fewer?		

Use vocabulary related to time; order days of the week

Building on previous learning

Before starting this unit check that the children can already:

☐ use everyday language related to time; order and sequence familiar events and measure short periods of time

Learning objectives

- Use vocabulary related to time
- Order days of the week

Learning outcomes

The children will be able to:

- use vocabulary related to time
- say the names of the days of the week in order
- arrange the days of the week in the correct order on the screen

Success criteria

Can the children…

☐ talk about events using the appropriate vocabulary?

☐ sort the days of the week into the correct order?

How to use the material for discussion

The children will be familiar with the days of the week though some will not remember the order. This activity gives practice in reading the names of the days, in arranging the days in order and also in using a wide range of vocabulary related to time. You may wish to discuss specific events that happen on particular days to ensure that the activity is relevant to the children.

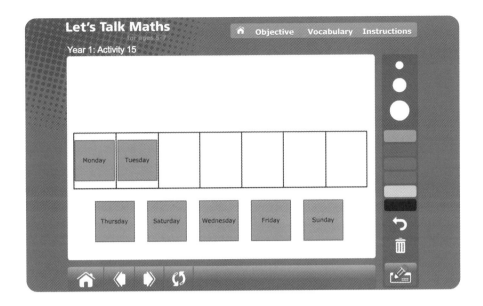

Starting with the chart blank, discuss the names of the days with the children. Ask them what day it is today. Drag today's card to the first box of the chart. Use this as the basis for adding the other days to the chart, all the time using the appropriate vocabulary.

Now encourage one of the children to lead the discussion by picking a day to place in the first box of the chart.

Appropriate vocabulary

day	week	Monday
Tuesday	Wednesday	Thursday
Friday	Saturday	Sunday
morning	afternoon	evening
night	above	below
before	after	today
tomorrow	yesterday	next

Use vocabulary related to time; order months of the year

Building on previous learning

Before starting this unit check that the children can already:

☐ use everyday language related to time; order and sequence familiar events and measure short periods of time

☐ order days of the week

Learning objectives

■ Use vocabulary related to time

■ Order months of the year

Learning outcomes

The children will be able to:

■ use vocabulary related to time

■ say the months of the year in order

■ arrange the months of the year in the correct order on the screen

Success criteria

Can the children…

☐ talk about events using the appropriate vocabulary?

☐ sort the months of the year into the correct order?

How to use the material for discussion

Most children will know the names of the months of the year but will not know the order in which they come. This activity gives practice in reading the names of the months, in arranging the months in order and also in using a wide range of vocabulary related to time. You may wish to discuss specific events that happen in particular months, such as pupils' birthdays, festivals, etc, to ensure that the activity is relevant to the children.

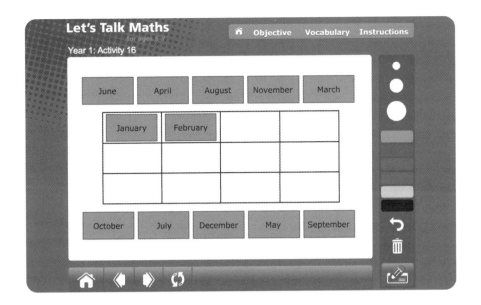

Starting with the chart blank, discuss the names of the months with the children. Ask them what the current month is. Drag this month's card to the appropriate position on the chart – the months should be arranged in order from January to December, and this gives the opportunity for using the vocabulary of ordinal number: ie, first, second, third, etc. Use this month's position on the chart as the basis for adding the other months, all the time using the appropriate vocabulary.

Now clear the chart and encourage one of the children to lead the discussion by picking a month to place in the appropriate position.

Appropriate vocabulary

month	above	below
before	after	year
January, February, etc	first, second, third, etc	next
spring	summer	autumn
winter	halfway	last

Use the vocabulary of halves and quarters in context

Building on previous learning

Before starting this unit check that the children can already:

☐ use language such as 'circle' or 'bigger' to describe the shape and size of solids and flat shapes

☐ identify shapes such as squares, rectangles, triangles and circles

Learning objectives

■ Use the vocabulary of halves in context

■ Use the vocabulary of quarters in context

Learning outcomes

The children will be able to:

■ use the vocabulary of halves when discussing 2-D shapes such as circles and squares

■ use the vocabulary of quarters when discussing 2-D shapes such as circles and squares

Success criteria

Can the children…

☐ discuss portions of pizzas, cakes, etc using the term 'half' appropriately?

☐ discuss portions of pizzas, cakes, etc using the term 'quarter' appropriately?

How to use the material for discussion

Before doing the activity, take the opportunity to discuss halves and quarters with the child using a real food item such as an apple.

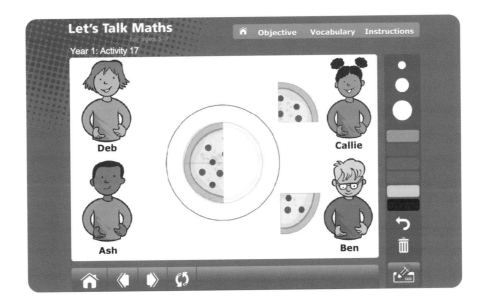

Discuss the scene with the children, using vocabulary such as 'whole' and 'share'. Ask the children how much of the pizza each child should have. You can drag the pizza slices so that two of the children have a quarter of the pizza each and one child has half of the pizza but one child has nothing. This will give opportunities to discuss equal sharing, who has more, who has less, etc.

Appropriate vocabulary

problem	question	answer
explain	count	compare
more	less	how much more?
how much less?	share	altogether
equal	fraction	half
quarter	whole	fair

Read the time to the hour and half-hour

Building on previous learning

Before starting this unit check that the children can already:

☐ use everyday language related to time; order and sequence familiar events and measure short periods of time

Learning objectives

- Read the time to the hour
- Read the time to the half-hour

Learning outcomes

The children will be able to:

- use the vocabulary related to time
- read the time to the hour
- read the time to the half-hour

Success criteria

Can the children...

☐ identify the times shown on the clocks as they appear on the presentation?

☐ use appropriate vocabulary to discuss the times?

☐ relate specific times of day to their own lives?

How to use the material for discussion

Before doing the activity, take the opportunity to discuss times of day that are relevant to the children, eg the start of school, lunch-time, end of school, bed time, etc.

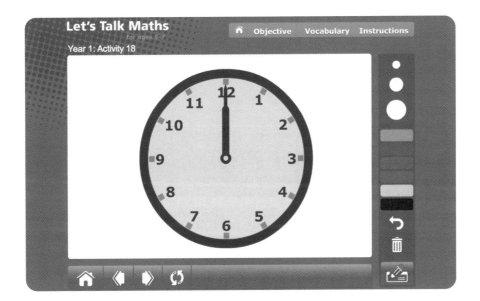

Discuss the time shown on the clock pointing out the positions of the hour hand and minute hand, particularly on the 'half-past' times. Invite the children to click on the clock to display new times and to take turns to lead the discussion.

Appropriate vocabulary

time	clock	hands
morning	afternoon	evening
midnight	mid-day	noon
hour	night	day
before	after	whole turn
half turn	o'clock	half-past

Read and compare two-digit numbers

Building on previous learning

Before starting this unit check that the children can already:

- [ ] read and write numerals from 0 to 20, then beyond
- [ ] use knowledge of place value to position these numbers on a number track or number line
- [ ] say the number that is 1 more or 1 less than any given number
- [ ] say the number that is 10 more or 10 less than a multiple of 10

Learning objectives

- Read two-digit numbers
- Compare two-digit numbers
- Use the greater than (>) and less than (<) signs

Learning outcomes

The children will be able to:

- read any two-digit number
- relate all these to the number line
- talk confidently about the numbers
- compare any pair of numbers and use the > and < signs

Success criteria

Can the children...

- [ ] read confidently the numbers pointed out to them?
- [ ] listen and talk confidently using some of the vocabulary listed and some of the question types shown?
- [ ] say which number is bigger or smaller when comparing two numbers?
- [ ] use the greater than or less than signs?

How to use the material for discussion

Talk about the numbers and symbols displayed. The adult should start with asking questions to provide a structure but should try to withdraw from the discussion and allow the children to take over so that they are asking questions of each other. They will, at times, need to be reminded of the appropriate vocabulary and you may wish to encourage them to use the vocabulary listed.

Some children find the use of the greater than and less than signs very difficult. These children may still be able to identify each two-digit number and to compare one with another orally.

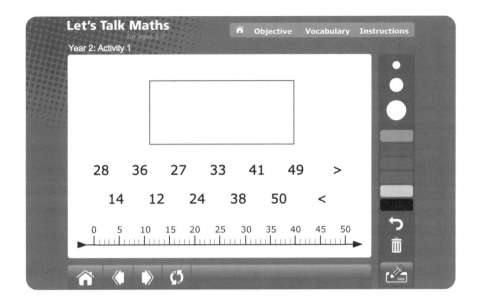

Drag one of the numbers to the centre box then open the activity with questions of the following type:

- What is this number? Can you read this number?
- How many digits does this number have?

Now ask the children to take turns to drag a number to the box and to ask similar questions of the others.

When the children are confident, introduce the > and < signs and use them to compare a pair of two-digit numbers by dragging two numbers and one of the signs to the centre box. Some children find it helpful to consider each sign as a crocodile's open mouth – the open mouth is always towards the 'biggest meal' – others notice that the sign is narrowing to a small point at one end and that the small point will be nearest the smallest number. Again, invite the children to take turns to 'lead' the discussion.

Appropriate vocabulary

show me	read	sign
compare	order	more
less	bigger	smaller
larger	greater than	smaller than
before	after	symbol
'teens' number	explain	digit

Describe and extend number sequences and recognise odd and even numbers

Building on previous learning

Before starting this unit check that the children can already:

- [ ] read and write numerals from 0 to 20, then beyond
- [ ] use knowledge of place value to position these numbers on a number track and number line
- [ ] read and write two-digit numbers in figures and words
- [ ] count on or back in ones, twos, fives and tens and use this knowledge to derive the multiples of 2, 5 and 10 to the tenth multiple

Learning objectives

- Describe number sequences
- Extend number sequences
- Recognise multiples of 2, 5 and 10
- Recognise odd and even numbers

Learning outcomes

The children will be able to:

- read all numerals from 0 to 40
- relate all these to the number line
- state the number that is 1 more or 1 less than a specified number
- state the number that is 10 more or 10 less than a multiple of 10
- use appropriate vocabulary
- talk confidently about the numbers

Success criteria

Can the children...

- [ ] read confidently the numbers pointed out to them?
- [ ] describe and extend a number sequence that is started for them?
- [ ] identify the odd and even numbers?
- [ ] identify the multiples of 2, 5 or 10?

How to use the material for discussion

The collection of numbers on the screen allows you to explore several aspects of maths with the children, all the time encouraging the use of appropriate vocabulary.

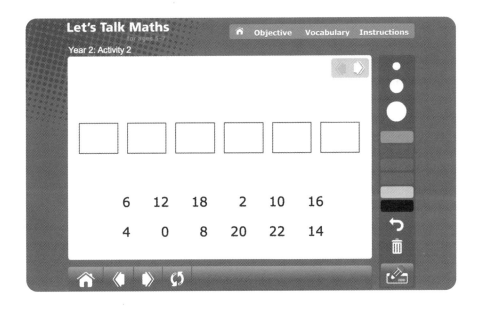

Drag one of the numbers into the first box and discuss it with questions such as:

● What is this number? Is it odd or even?

● How many digits does this number have?

Now choose a number to fit in the second box and ask the children to compare it to the first number – eg it could be 2 more than the first number. Ask the children what number to drag in next that will be 2 more than the last number. Repeat this until all the six boxes are occupied.

As part of your work for Block B, sort the numbers into three different areas of the screen: multiples of 2, multiples of 5 and multiples of 10. You may like to sort the numbers into two different areas of the screen: odd numbers and even numbers.

Appropriate vocabulary

show me	read	continue
compare	order	more
less	biggest	smallest
before	after	sequence
'teens' number	explain	digit
odd	even	pattern
predict	reason	relationship
sort	classify	

Count up to 100 objects by grouping them and counting in tens, fives or twos

Building on previous learning

Before starting this unit check that the children can already:

☐ read and write two-digit numbers in figures and words

☐ count on or back in ones, twos, fives and tens and use this knowledge to derive the multiples of 2, 5 and 10 to the tenth multiple

Learning objectives

- Estimate a number of objects
- Count up to 100 objects by grouping them and counting in tens, fives or twos

Learning outcomes

The children will be able to:

- estimate a number of objects, saying that the number is 'roughly ...'
- count the objects by grouping them in twos, fives or tens

Success criteria

Can the children...

☐ give confidently a rough approximation of the number of objects shown on the screen?

☐ use strategies of counting involving drawing rings around the objects to enable them to be counted in twos, fives or tens?

How to use the material for discussion

This activity provides practice in estimation, in recognising and remembering the multiples of 2, 5 and 10 and in using appropriate strategies for counting large numbers of items. As with all of these activities the children will gain most benefit if they are encouraged to discuss what they are doing - for this purpose you may wish to ask the children to take turns to 'lead' the activity.

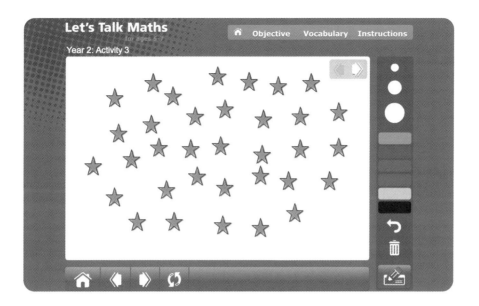

A number of stars are displayed. Discourage the children from counting the stars, ask them to make an estimate instead. Now invite one of the children to draw rings around the stars in groups of two, five or ten and help the children to count them.

Now click on the top right hand arrow and ask one of the children to lead the activity by estimating a new number of stars.

Appropriate vocabulary

one, two, three, ... hundred	estimate	roughly
group	odd	even
compare	partition	

Use a hundred square for adding or subtracting mentally a one-digit number or a multiple of 10 from any two-digit number

Building on previous learning

Before starting this unit check that the children can already:

☐ derive and recall all pairs of numbers with a total of 10

☐ derive and recall addition facts for totals to at least 5 and work out the corresponding subtraction facts

☐ count on or back in ones, twos, fives and tens

☐ relate addition to counting on; understand subtraction as take away and find a difference by counting up

Learning objectives

■ Add mentally a one-digit number to any two-digit number

■ Add mentally a multiple of 10 to any two-digit number

■ Subtract mentally a one-digit number from any two-digit number

■ Subtract mentally a multiple of 10 from any two-digit number

Learning outcomes

The children will be able to:

■ use the hundred square to add mentally a one-digit number to any two-digit number

■ use the hundred square to add mentally a multiple of 10 to any two-digit number

■ use the hundred square to subtract mentally a one-digit number from any two-digit number

■ use the hundred square to subtract mentally a multiple of 10 from any two-digit number

Success criteria

Can the children…

☐ use the hundred square to assist them to add or subtract mentally a one-digit number or a multiple of 10 to or from any two-digit number?

☐ use appropriate vocabulary to describe and explain the processes?

☐ recognise that addition involves numbers to the right of the start number and subtraction involves numbers to the left but that crossing the tens boundary presents special conditions?

☐ recognise that addition or subtraction of multiples of ten involves numbers vertically below or above the start number on the square?

How to use the material for discussion

After starting the discussion by questioning the pupils yourself, encourage individual pupils to ask questions of the group. Ensure that all pupils use appropriate vocabulary.

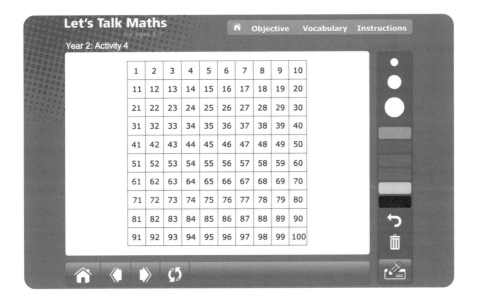

Start with some introductory activities, eg:

● Let's start on number 45. What is 45 add 3? or What is 45 plus 3? or What number is 3 more than 45?

Encourage the pupils to notice that adding 'goes to the right' but be careful when questions result in crossing the tens boundary, eg 38 + 5 To demonstrate these questions you may wish to use the number track from Year 1 Activity 3.

Now ask questions such as:

● What is 45 take away 3? What is 45 minus 3? What is 45 subtract 3?

Encourage the pupils to notice that subtracting 'goes to the left' but be careful when questions result in crossing the tens boundary, eg 51 - 5 To demonstrate these questions you may wish to use the number track from Year 1 Activity 3.

When the pupils are confident, repeat the activity by adding 10 to any number, then subtracting 10, then adding or subtracting multiples of 10, encouraging them to notice that these calculations involve numbers vertically below or above the start number.

Ensure that you provide the pupils with opportunities to take turns to 'be the teacher' asking the questions of the others.

Note that some children experience confusion with the hundred square because 'higher' numbers appear physically lower on the square: eg, 53 is a higher number than 33 but appears two rows below it on the hundred square.

Appropriate vocabulary

zero, one, two, ..., hundred	add	plus
subtract	minus	equals
take away	leaves	difference
makes	operation	number sentence
tens boundary	calculate	mental calculation
correct	right	wrong

Read and compare three-digit numbers

Building on previous learning

Before starting this unit check that the children can already:

- [ ] Read two-digit numbers
- [ ] Compare two-digit numbers
- [ ] Use the greater than (>) and less than (<) signs

Learning objectives

- Read three-digit numbers
- Compare three-digit numbers
- Use the greater than (>) and less than (<) signs

Learning outcomes

The children will be able to:

- read any three-digit number
- relate all these to the number line
- talk confidently about the numbers
- compare any pair of numbers and use the > and < signs

Success criteria

Can the children…

- [ ] read confidently the numbers pointed out to them?
- [ ] listen and talk confidently using some of the vocabulary listed and some of the question types shown?
- [ ] say which number is bigger or smaller when comparing two numbers?
- [ ] use the greater than or less than signs?

How to use the material for discussion

Talk about the numbers and symbols displayed. The adult should start with asking questions to provide a structure but should try to withdraw from the discussion and allow the children to take over so that they are asking questions of each other. They will, at times, need to be reminded of the appropriate vocabulary and you may wish to encourage them to use the vocabulary listed.

Some children find the use of the greater than and less than signs very difficult. These children may still be able to identify each three-digit number and to compare one with another orally.

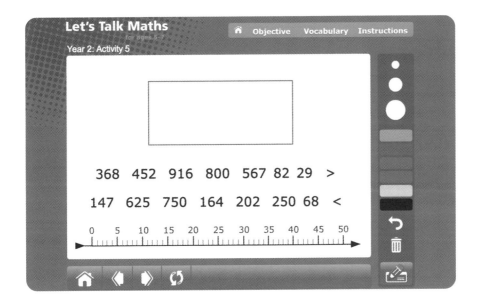

Drag one of the numbers to the centre box then open the activity with questions of the following type:

● What is this number? Can you read this number?
● How many digits does this number have?

Now ask the children to take turns to drag a number to the box and to ask similar questions of the others.

When the children are confident, introduce the > and < signs and use them to compare a pair of three-digit numbers by dragging two numbers and one of the signs to the centre box. Some children find it helpful to consider each sign as a crocodile's open mouth – the open mouth is always towards the 'biggest meal' – others notice that the sign is narrowing to a small point at one end and that the small point will be nearest the smallest number. Again, invite the children to take turns to 'lead' the discussion.

Appropriate vocabulary

show me	read	sign
compare	order	more
less	bigger	smaller
larger	greater than	smaller than
before	after	symbol
'teens' number	explain	digit

Solve problems involving adding, subtracting or multiplying in the context of numbers or money

Building on previous learning

Before starting this unit check that the children can already:

☐ add mentally a one-digit number or a multiple of 10 to any two-digit number

☐ subtract mentally a one-digit number or a multiple of 10 from any two-digit number

☐ solve problems involving adding or subtracting in the context of money with total amounts of at least 20p

Learning objectives

■ Solving problems involving adding, subtracting, multiplying or dividing in the context of money

Learning outcomes

The children will be able to:

■ find total amounts to pay for two items

■ find change when buying an item

■ find total amounts to pay for five equally priced articles

Success criteria

Can the children…

☐ add together two sums of money in pence to find the total cost of two priced items?

☐ find the change from 50 pence or £1 when buying some priced items?

☐ multiply a specified amount by 5?

☐ use appropriate vocabulary in relation to spending money and finding change?

How to use the material for discussion

The priced items on the presentation can be used for a variety of problem-solving questions: for comparing prices, for finding the total cost of two or more items, for finding change from 10p, 20p, 50p or £1. You may like to drag the items to the centre of the screen, together with an appropriate mathematical symbol to demonstrate the recording of each question.

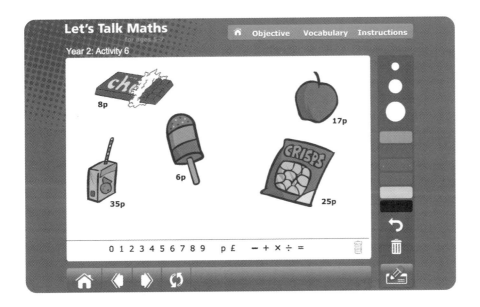

Discuss the items using questions such as:

- Which costs more, the drink or the crisps?
- How much more does an apple cost than a bar of chocolate?
- What is the difference in price between an apple and a packet of crisps?
- What is the total cost of a bar of chocolate and an apple?
- If I buy a carton of juice, how much change would I have from 50p?
- If I buy an ice cream, how much change would I have from £1?

Now encourage one of the pupils to ask some questions about buying the items.

You may wish to ask the children to find the cost of five bars of chocolate or five ice creams.

Appropriate vocabulary

more	less	total
cost	altogether	difference
price	change	double
answer	explain	operation

Derive and recall all addition and subtraction facts for each number to at least 10

Building on previous learning

Before starting this unit check that the children can already:

- [ ] count reliably at least 20 objects, recognising that when rearranged the number of objects stays the same
- [ ] compare and order numbers, using the related vocabulary
- [ ] use the vocabulary related to addition and subtraction and symbols to describe and record addition and subtraction number sentences
- [ ] use the equals sign

Learning objectives

- Derive and recall all addition and subtraction facts for numbers with a total of 6, 7, 8 or 9
- Use the vocabulary related to addition, subtraction and symbols to describe and record addition number sentences
- Use the equals sign

Learning outcomes

The children will be able to:

- recall all pairs of numbers with a total of 6, 7, 8 or 9
- write addition number sentences and the related subtraction sentences

Success criteria

Can the children...

- [ ] create number sentences on screen using the numerals and symbols?
- [ ] find all of the combinations of pairs of numbers that have a total of 6, 7, 8 or 9?
- [ ] find related subtraction facts?

How to use the material for discussion

This activity concerns raising pupils' confidence in mental arithmetic skills. Practising number facts, understanding the vocabulary and methods of recording, can give pupils the tools with which to deal with more complex mathematical problems.

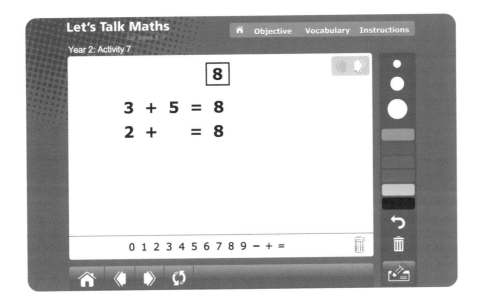

Discuss the number 8 with the children. Explain that they will be finding pairs of numbers that make 8 altogether. You could use a range of vocabulary to describe this, eg: finding two numbers that add together to equal 8, finding two numbers that have a total of 8, finding two numbers that have a sum of 8. Encourage the children to find as many number pairs as possible. Now ask them to find some subtractions to match the additions, using vocabulary such as 'inverse'. For example, alongside 3 + 5 = 8 they could show 8 - 5 = 3 or 8 - 3 = 5.

Ask the children to take turns to come to the whiteboard to drag a number up from the bank at the bottom of the screen to start a number sentence. Ask the first child to ask another one what to put next, ie the + sign or the - sign, then to ask another child what number should be put next, etc. Inform the children that today you will only be looking at subtracting a smaller number from a larger number. As with all of these activities, encourage each child to ask the questions clearly using the appropriate vocabulary.

Once all the children have found all the addition and subtraction facts for 8, ask them to find the addition and subtraction facts for 6, 7 and 9.

Appropriate vocabulary

zero, one, two, …, hundred	count	pair
more	less	larger
bigger	greater	fewer
smaller	add	more
plus	make	sum
total	altogether	equals
sign	explain	number sentence
write	record	the same number as
calculate	calculation	operation
answer	inverse	pattern

Derive and recall all addition and subtraction facts for pairs of numbers with a total of 20

Building on previous learning

Before starting this unit check that the children can already:

- [ ] count reliably at least 20 objects, recognising that when rearranged the number of objects stays the same
- [ ] compare and order numbers, using the related vocabulary
- [ ] use the vocabulary related to addition and subtraction and symbols to describe and record addition and subtraction number sentences
- [ ] use the equals sign

Learning objectives

- Derive and recall all addition and subtraction facts for numbers with a total of 20
- Use the vocabulary related to addition, subtraction and symbols to describe and record addition number sentences
- Use the equals sign

Learning outcomes

The children will be able to:

- recall all pairs of numbers with a total of 20
- write addition number sentences and the related subtraction sentences

Success criteria

Can the children…

- [ ] create number sentences on screen using the numerals and symbols?
- [ ] find all of the combinations of pairs of numbers that have a total of 20?
- [ ] find related subtraction facts?

How to use the material for discussion

This activity concerns raising pupils' confidence in mental arithmetic skills. Practising number facts, understanding the vocabulary and methods of recording, can give pupils the tools with which to deal with more complex mathematical problems.

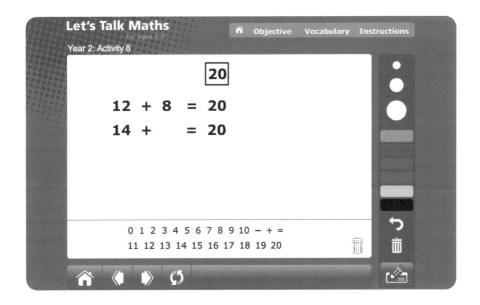

Discuss the number 20 with the children. Explain that they will be finding pairs of numbers that make 20 altogether. Encourage the children to find as many number pairs as possible. Now ask them to find some subtractions to match the additions, using vocabulary such as 'inverse'. For example, alongside 12 + 8 = 20 they could show 20 - 8 = 12 or 20 - 12 = 8.

Ask the children to take turns to come to the screen to drag a number up from the bottom of the screen to start a number sentence. Ask the first child to ask another one what to put next, ie the + sign or the - sign, then to ask another child what number should be put next, etc. Inform the children that today you will only be looking at adding pairs that make 20 and at subtracting from 20. As with all of these activities, encourage each child to ask the questions clearly using the appropriate vocabulary.

Appropriate vocabulary

zero, one, two, ..., hundred	count	pair
more	less	larger
bigger	greater	fewer
smaller	add	more
plus	make	sum
total	altogether	equals
sign	explain	number sentence
write	record	the same number as
calculate	calculation	operation
answer	inverse	pattern

Year 2 Activity 9

Derive and recall all addition and subtraction facts for pairs of multiples of 10 up to 100

Building on previous learning

Before starting this unit check that the children can already:

☐ read and compare two-digit numbers, using the related vocabulary

☐ use the vocabulary related to addition and subtraction and symbols to describe and record addition and subtraction number sentences

☐ use the equals sign

Learning objectives

■ Derive and recall all addition and subtraction facts for all pairs of multiples of 10 up to 100

■ Use the vocabulary related to addition, subtraction and symbols to describe and record addition number sentences

■ Use the equals sign

Learning outcomes

The children will be able to:

■ derive all addition and subtraction facts for all pairs of multiples of 10 up to 100

■ recall all addition and subtraction facts for all pairs of multiples of 10 up to 100

■ write addition number sentences and the related subtraction sentences

Success criteria

Can the children…

☐ create number sentences on screen using the numerals and symbols?

☐ find all of the combinations of pairs of multiples of 10 up to 100?

☐ find related subtraction facts?

How to use the material for discussion

This activity concerns raising pupils' confidence in mental arithmetic skills. Practising number facts, understanding the vocabulary and methods of recording, can give pupils the tools with which to deal with more complex mathematical problems. Knowledge of the number facts for multiples of 10 is helpful to pupils when they are working with money or measurements.

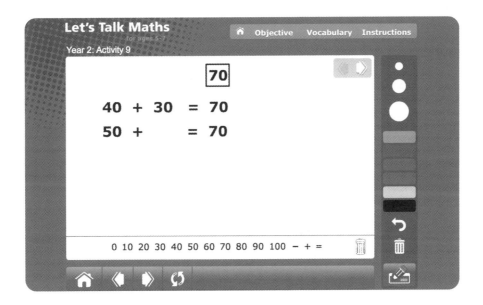

Discuss the number 70 with the children. Explain that they will be finding pairs of numbers that make 70 altogether. Encourage the children to find as many number pairs as possible. Now ask them to find some subtractions to match the additions, using vocabulary such as 'inverse'. For example, alongside 40 + 30 = 70 they could show 70 - 40 = 30 and 70 - 30 = 40.

Ask the children to take turns to come to the screen to drag a number up from the bank at the bottom of the screen to start a number sentence. Ask the first child to ask another one what to put next, ie the + sign or the - sign, then to ask another child what number should be put next, etc. Inform the children that today you will only be looking at subtracting a smaller number from a larger number. As with all of these activities, encourage each child to ask the questions clearly using the appropriate vocabulary.

Once all the children have found the addition facts and subtraction facts for 20, ask them to find the addition and subtraction facts for 80 and 90.

Appropriate vocabulary

zero, one, two, ..., hundred	count	pair
more	less	larger
bigger	greater	fewer
smaller	add	more
plus	make	sum
total	altogether	equals
sign	explain	number sentence
write	record	the same number as
calculate	calculation	operation
answer	inverse	pattern

Derive and recall multiplication facts for the 2 times table and related division facts

Building on previous learning

Before starting this unit check that the children can already:

☐ read and compare two-digit numbers, using the related vocabulary

☐ count on or back in ones, twos, fives and tens and use this knowledge to derive the multiples of 2, 5 and 10 to the tenth multiple

Learning objectives

- derive multiplication facts for the 2 times table

- use the symbols x and = to record and interpret number sentences involving multiplication

- recall multiplication facts for the 2 times table

- derive division facts related to the 2 times table

- use the symbols ÷ and = to record and interpret number sentences involving division

- recall division facts related to the 2 times table

Learning outcomes

The children will be able to:

- derive and recall all multiplication and division facts for the 2 times table

- use the symbols x and = to record and interpret number sentences involving multiplication

- use the symbols ÷ and = to record and interpret number sentences involving division

Success criteria

Can the children...

☐ create number sentences on screen using the numerals and symbols to show the 2 times table?

☐ find related division facts?

How to use the material for discussion

This activity concerns raising pupils' confidence in mental arithmetic skills by constructing the 2 times table and finding the corresponding division facts. Practising number facts, understanding the vocabulary and methods of recording, can give pupils the tools with which to deal with more complex mathematical problems.

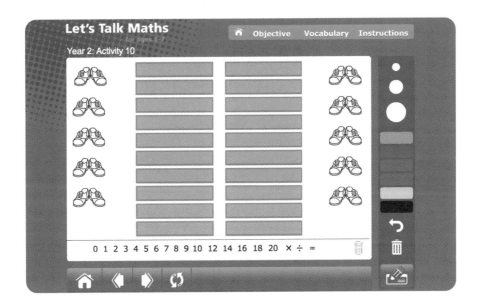

Discuss the pairs of shoes. Ask the children to take turns to record a part of the 2 times table. As with all of these activities, encourage each child to ask the questions clearly using the appropriate vocabulary.

Once the 2 times table is complete ask the children to find the corresponding division facts and to record these alongside, in the right hand column of the table.

Appropriate vocabulary

pair	multiply	divide
equals	times	share
sign	explain	number sentence
write	record	the same number as
calculate	calculation	operation
answer	inverse	pattern

Derive and recall multiplication facts for the 5 times table and related division facts

Building on previous learning

Before starting this unit check that the children can already:

☐ read and compare two-digit numbers, using the related vocabulary

☐ count on or back in ones, twos, fives and tens and use this knowledge to derive the multiples of 2, 5 and 10 to the tenth multiple

Learning objectives

- derive multiplication facts for the 5 times table

- use the symbols x and = to record and interpret number sentences involving multiplication

- recall multiplication facts for the 5 times table

- derive division facts related to the 5 times table

- use the symbols ÷ and = to record and interpret number sentences involving division

- recall division facts related to the 5 times table

Learning outcomes

The children will be able to:

- derive and recall all multiplication and division facts for the 5 times table

- use the symbols x and = to record and interpret number sentences involving multiplication

- use the symbols ÷ and = to record and interpret number sentences involving division

Success criteria

Can the children…

☐ create number sentences on screen using the numerals and symbols to show the 5 times table?

☐ find related division facts?

How to use the material for discussion

This activity concerns raising pupils' confidence in mental arithmetic skills by constructing the 5 times table and finding the corresponding division facts. Practising number facts, understanding the vocabulary and methods of recording, can give pupils the tools with which to deal with more complex mathematical problems.

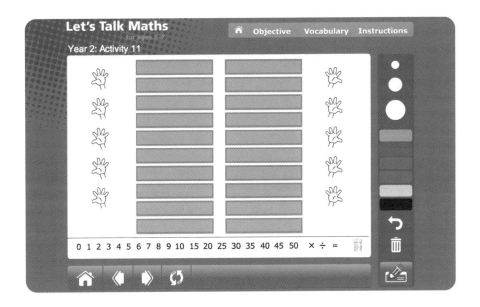

Discuss the hands. Ask the children to take turns to record a part of the 5 times table. As with all of these activities, encourage each child to ask the questions clearly using the appropriate vocabulary.

Once the 5 times table is complete ask the children to find the corresponding division facts and to record these alongside, in the right hand column of the table.

Appropriate vocabulary

pair	multiply	divide
equals	times	share
sign	explain	number sentence
write	record	the same number as
calculate	calculation	operation
answer	inverse	pattern

Derive and recall multiplication facts for the 10 times table and related division facts

Building on previous learning

Before starting this unit check that the children can already:

☐ read and compare two-digit numbers, using the related vocabulary

☐ count on or back in ones, twos, fives and tens and use this knowledge to derive the multiples of 2, 5 and 10 to the tenth multiple

Learning objectives

- derive multiplication facts for the 10 times table

- use the symbols x and = to record and interpret number sentences involving multiplication

- recall multiplication facts for the 10 times table

- derive division facts related to the 10 times table

- use the symbols ÷ and = to record and interpret number sentences involving division

- recall division facts related to the 10 times table

Learning outcomes

The children will be able to:

- derive and recall all multiplication and division facts for the 10 times table

- use the symbols x and = to record and interpret number sentences involving multiplication

- use the symbols ÷ and = to record and interpret number sentences involving division

Success criteria

Can the children…

☐ create number sentences on screen using the numerals and symbols to show the 10 times table?

☐ find related division facts?

How to use the material for discussion

This activity concerns raising pupils' confidence in mental arithmetic skills by constructing the 10 times table and finding the corresponding division facts. The 10 times table may seem obvious to us but some children do not understand it straight away and need support in recognising what it represents – the pictures of toes can help with this.

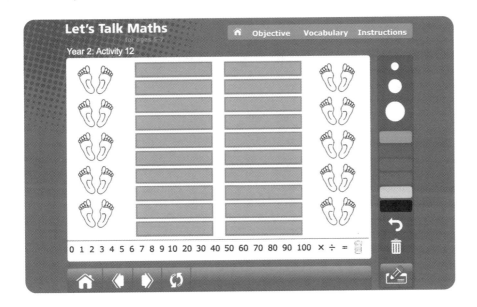

Discuss the toes. Ask the children to take turns to record a part of the 10 times table. As with all of these activities, encourage each child to ask the questions clearly using the appropriate vocabulary.

Once the 10 times table is complete ask the children to find the corresponding division facts and to record these alongside, in the right hand column of the table.

Appropriate vocabulary

pair	multiply	divide
equals	times	share
sign	explain	number sentence
write	record	the same number as
calculate	calculation	operation
answer	inverse	pattern

Year 2 Activity 13

Identify reflective symmetry in patterns and 2-D shapes

Building on previous learning

Before starting this unit check that the children can already:

☐ visualise and name common 2-D shapes and describe their features

Learning objectives

- Identifying reflective symmetry in patterns and 2-D shapes
- Visualising common 2-D shapes
- Identifying shapes from pictures of them in different positions and orientations
- Sorting, making and describing shapes referring to their properties

Learning outcomes

The children will be able to:

- create symmetrical pictures by combining two 'half' pictures
- use appropriate vocabulary to describe the symmetrical properties of the pictures
- use appropriate vocabulary to describe common 2-D shapes

Success criteria

Can the children...

☐ create symmetrical pictures, recognising why they are symmetrical?

☐ use appropriate vocabulary describe common 2-D shapes and the symmetrical properties of the pictures?

How to use the material for discussion

You may like to find and discuss symmetrical objects in the classroom with the children before you start the activity. Talk about symmetry in shapes.

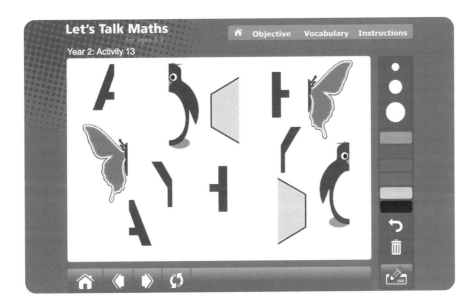

Invite pupils to come to the screen and drag the half-pictures to the centre to create a symmetrical picture. Encourage them to discuss the half-pictures and completed pictures, referring particularly to the symmetry of the completed pictures.

Appropriate vocabulary

triangle	quadrilateral	rectangle
hexagon	corner	side
straight	curved	shape
line of symmetry	mirror line	reflection

Year 2 Activity 14

Visualise common 2-D shapes; sort, make and describe shapes

Building on previous learning

Before starting this unit check that the children can already:

☐ visualise and name common 2-D shapes and describe their features

Learning objectives

- Identifying reflective symmetry in patterns and 2-D shapes
- Visualising common 2-D shapes
- Identifying shapes from pictures of them in different positions and orientations
- Sorting, making and describing shapes referring to their properties

Learning outcomes

The children will be able to:

- create 2-D shapes on screen
- use appropriate vocabulary to refer to the properties of the shapes
- visualise, make and describe the following shapes: square, triangle, rectangle, pentagon, hexagon, octagon

Success criteria

Can the children...

☐ create 2-D shapes, using appropriate vocabulary to refer to their properties?

☐ visualise, make and describe a square, triangle, rectangle, pentagon, hexagon and octagon?

How to use the material for discussion

You may like to allow the children some 'free play' with making shapes using the lines provided on the screen before they move on to creating the mathematical shapes. Practise using the appropriate vocabulary for giving instructions on how to sort, make and describe the shapes.

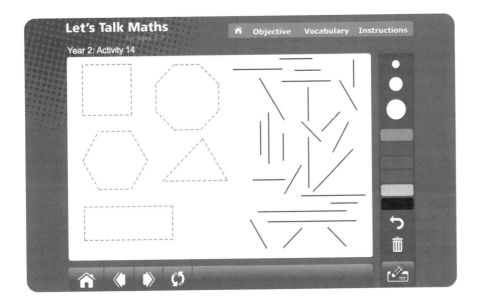

Invite the children to come to the whiteboard and drag lines onto the correct dotted outline to create different shapes. Once a shape has been correctly constructed, there is an opportunity for discussion: What is the name of this shape? What properties does a hexagon have?

Allow the children to take turns to lead the discussion by giving instructions to another pupil on which lines to choose to create a shape.

Appropriate vocabulary

triangle	quadrilateral	rectangle
hexagon	corner	side
straight	curved	shape
line of symmetry	mirror line	reflection
square	rectangular	triangular
pentagon	octagon	edge
property	explain	describe

Present and interpret outcomes using block graphs

Building on previous learning

Before starting this unit check that the children can already:

☐ answer a question by recording information in lists and tables

☐ present outcomes using pictograms or block graphs

Learning objectives

■ Solving problems involving adding in the context of numbers

■ Solving problems involving subtracting in the context of numbers

■ Presenting outcomes using block graphs

■ Answering a question by collecting and recording information in lists and tables

Learning outcomes

The children will be able to:

■ find totals in the context of methods of travel to school

■ make comparisons between different methods of travel

■ contribute to the creation of a block graph

■ interpret the information on a block graph

Success criteria

Can the children…

☐ contribute to the creation of a block graph?

☐ interpret the information on the block graph?

☐ use appropriate vocabulary when interpreting data?

How to use the material for discussion

Before doing the activity, discuss collecting information about methods of travel to school. Ask the children to state whether they travel on foot, by bike, by car, by bus, by train, by taxi or by any other method. Gather the information on a table or chart for the children to refer to when you discuss the creation of the block graph.

This activity follows on from work in Year 1 and you may like to use Year 1 Activity 14 with the children as extra practice.

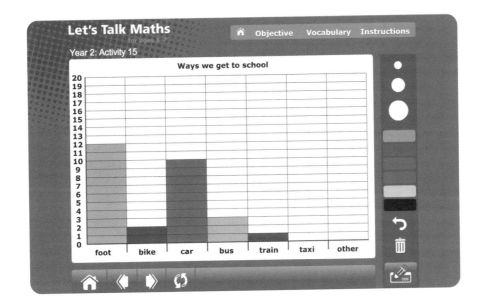

Invite pupils to come to the screen and enter the data that you have collected so that the block graph is completed. Ask questions about the graph, eg:

- How many people travel to school by bus?
- What is the most common method of travel to school?
- What is the least common method of travel to school?
- Why are some columns empty?
- If we asked all the teachers, what do you think would be the most common method of travel that they use to get to school? Is that the same as your most common method of travel to school?

Appropriate vocabulary

problem	question	collect
organise	compare	order
sort	group	different
represent	interpret	count
tally	information	graph
block graph	list	table
label	title	more
less	most common	least common
most popular	least popular	how many more?
how many fewer?		

Recognise and use whole, half and quarter turns, both clockwise and anticlockwise

Building on previous learning

Before starting this unit check that the children can already:

- [ ] identify objects that turn about a point (eg scissors) or about a line (eg a door)
- [ ] recognise and make whole, half and quarter turns

Learning objectives

- Recognise and use whole, half and quarter turns, both clockwise and anticlockwise
- Know that a right angle represents a quarter turn
- Follow and give instructions involving position, direction and movement

Learning outcomes

The children will be able to:

- recognise whole, half and quarter turns
- understand and use the terms clockwise and anticlockwise
- know that a right angle represents a quarter turn
- follow and give instructions involving position, direction and movement in relation to rotation around a central point

Success criteria

Can the children...

- [ ] show whole, half and quarter turns?
- [ ] use appropriate vocabulary to discuss the rotations?
- [ ] follow and give instructions involving position, direction and movement in relation to rotation around a central point?

How to use the material for discussion

Practise turns in the classroom: Stand up and face the whiteboard. Turn all the way round so that you end up facing the whiteboard again, etc.

Introduce the 'spinner' to the children, showing them how the arrow rotates about the centre of the circle.

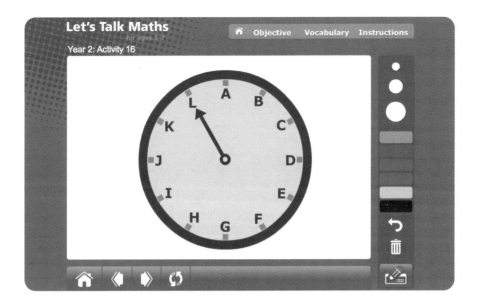

Start the discussion by pointing the spinner's arrow to a random letter. Invite one of the children to turn the arrow around the circle back to the start letter. Ask the others which way the child rotated the arrow, clockwise or anticlockwise.

Now ask one of the children to come out to lead the activity. Encourage them to ask others to turn the arrow through a half turn.

Move on to considering quarter turns.

Appropriate vocabulary

direction	clockwise	anticlockwise
rotate	rotation	turn
whole	half	quarter
right angle	centre	circle

Read the time to the hour, half-hour and quarter hour

Building on previous learning

Before starting this unit check that the children can already:

☐ use everyday language related to time; order and sequence familiar events and measure short periods of time

☐ read time to the hour and half-hour

Learning objectives

■ Read the time to the hour

■ Read the time to the half-hour

■ Read 'quarter past' times

■ Read 'quarter to' times

Learning outcomes

The children will be able to:

■ use the vocabulary related to time

■ read the time to the hour

■ read the time to the half-hour

■ read the time to the quarter-hour

Success criteria

Can the children...

☐ identify the times shown on the clocks as they appear on the presentation?

☐ use appropriate vocabulary to discuss the times?

☐ relate specific times of day to their own lives?

How to use the material for discussion

Discuss times of day that are relevant to the children, eg the start of school, lunch-time, end of school, bed time, etc.

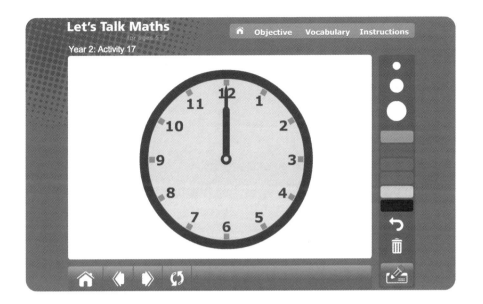

Discuss the time shown on the clock pointing out the positions of the hour hand and minute hand, particularly on the 'quarter' or 'half-past' times. Invite the children to click the clock face to display new times and to take turns to lead the discussion.

Appropriate vocabulary

time	clock	hands
morning	afternoon	evening
midnight	mid-day	noon
hour	night	day
before	after	whole turn
half turn	o'clock	half-past
quarter to	quarter past	minute
second	analogue	digital
watch		

Discussion Focus 18: Derive and recall doubles of all numbers to 20

Building on previous learning

Before starting this unit check that the children can already:

☐ derive and recall multiplication facts for the 2 times-table

☐ recall the doubles of all numbers to at least 10

Learning objectives

- Derive doubles of all numbers to 20
- Recall doubles of all numbers to 20

Learning outcomes

The children will be able to:

- find the double of any number from 0 to 20
- remember the double of any number from 0 to 20

Success criteria

Can the children…

☐ find the double of any number from 0 to 20?

☐ remember the double of any number from 0 to 20?

How to use the material for discussion

This activity gives the opportunity to strengthen mental maths skills using a range of strategies that children can explain to each other. It is suitable for repeated use to provide practice.

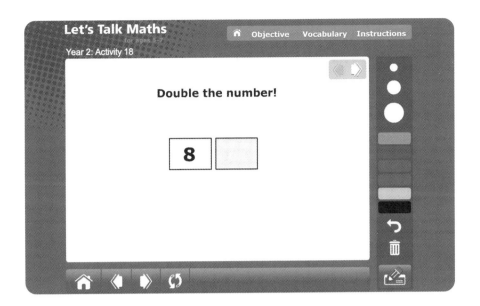

Ask the children to double the number on screen and then click on the box to reveal the answer. Each child should take a turn at leading the discussion. Encourage them to explain the strategies they use, particularly for the larger numbers. For example, to double 19 some children may double 10 then double 9 and add the answers; others may double 20 then subtract 2 (but watch this carefully, as some will double 20 then only subtract 1). Do the children notice that all the answers are even numbers?

Appropriate vocabulary

calculate	double	answer
method	explain	predict
pattern	add	plus
operation	equals	number sentence
count on	equal groups of	multiplied by

Understand that halving is the inverse of doubling

Building on previous learning

Before starting this unit check that the children can already:

☐ derive and recall multiplication facts for the 2 times-table

☐ derive and recall doubles of all numbers to 20

Learning objectives

- Understand that halving is the inverse of doubling
- Derive and recall doubles of all numbers to 20
- Derive and recall the corresponding halves

Learning outcomes

The children will be able to:

- find the double of any number from 0 to 20
- remember the double of any number from 0 to 20
- find half of any even number from 2 to 40
- remember half of any even number from 2 to 40

Success criteria

Can the children…

☐ find the double of any number from 0 to 20?

☐ remember the double of any number from 0 to 20?

☐ find half of any even number from 2 to 40?

☐ remember half of any even number from 2 to 40?

How to use the material for discussion

This activity gives the opportunity to strengthen mental maths skills using a range of strategies that children can explain to each other. It is suitable for repeated use to provide practice.

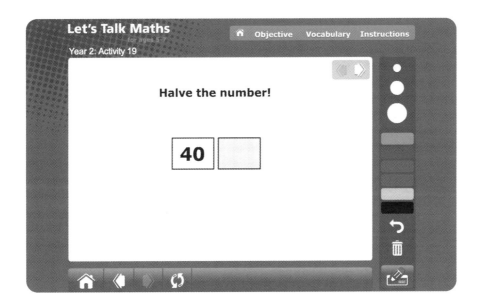

Ask the children to halve the number displayed on the screen and then click the box to reveal the answer. Each child should take a turn at leading the discussion. Encourage them to explain the strategies they use, particularly for the larger numbers. For example, to halve 38 some children may halve 20, then halve 10, then halve 8, then add the answers. Do the children notice that the numbers to halve are all even numbers but that not all the answers are even numbers?

Appropriate vocabulary

calculate	double	answer
method	explain	predict
pattern	add	plus
divide	divided by	halve
operation	equals	number sentence
count back	equal groups of	share equally
equal parts	division	fraction

Published 2009 by A & C Black Publishers Limited
36 Soho Square, London W1D 3QY
www.acblack.com

ISBN 9781408110645

Copyright © A & C Black Publishers Limited
Written by Andrew Brodie
Page layout by Bob Vickers

A CIP record for this publication is available from the British Library.

Printed in Great Britain by Martins the Printers, Berwick-upon-Tweed.

This book is produced using paper that is made from wood grown in
managed, sustainable forests. It is natural, renewable and recyclable.
The logging and manufacturing processes conform to the environmental
regulations of the country of origin.

To see our full range of titles visit www.acblack.com